YOUNG PEOPLE, HOMELESSNESS AND HIV / AIDS

Issues from a national consultation exercise involving the statutory and voluntary sectors

Edited by: Peter Aggleton and Ian Warwick

for the Health Education Authority

A CIP catalogue record for this book
is available from the British Library.

Published in 1992

Health Education Authority
Hamilton House
Mabledon Place
London WC1H 9TX

ISBN 1 85448 408 7

Typeset by DP Photosetting, Aylesbury, Bucks
Printed and bound in Great Britain by
KPC Group

Acknowledgements

The Health Education Authority gratefully acknowledges the help received from many individuals and organisations in the preparation of this report.

In particular, thanks are due to Peter Aggleton, Ian Warwick and the rest of the team at Goldsmiths' College, to all those who took part in the consultation process and to all those who took time to comment on the consultation report.

Hannah Cinamon
Programme Officer
HIV/AIDS and Sexual Health Programme
Health Education Authority

Contents

Introduction

In the continued absence of a vaccine to prevent infection and of drugs which offer a cure for HIV disease, health education continues to be the most effective way of responding to AIDS. Six years after the first public information campaigns were launched in Britain, knowledge levels are high amongst most adults and most young people. Whilst behaviour change towards safer sex is uneven, suggesting that more than the facts is needed for people to change their behaviour, the foundations for future work have been laid. It is therefore important to turn our attention to those 'hard to reach' settings and those 'hard to reach' groups which have been overlooked by past and present initiatives.

Throughout the 1980s and into the 1990s, homelessness in Britain has risen dramatically to become an issue of national concern. Shelter has recently estimated that there are 150 000 homeless young people in Britain, of whom two-thirds live outside London. Many sleep rough, squat or stay in derelict buildings. Some are malnourished and suffer from prolonged ill-health. Others may become involved in youth prostitution as a means of earning money. A few may inject drugs. All are vulnerable to assault, discrimination and abuse (Centrepoint, 1989; Young Homelessness Group, 1990). Recent work undertaken for the World Health Organisation in Europe highlights the need for national governments, health and local authorities, and non-governmental organisations to consider the steps they can take to provide homeless young people with HIV/AIDS education (WHO, 1990). This is particularly important since many of those concerned may be cut off from mainstream channels of communication such as television, radio, newspapers and magazines, schools and youth clubs.

It was within the above context that the Health Education Authority commissioned a series of consultative meetings to bring together key policy makers and practitioners to clarify the issues to be addressed. The first meeting was held in May 1990 at Regents College, London, for workers in non-statutory groups and organisations. Subsequent meetings were held in July and September 1991 at the King's Fund Centre for representatives of relevant professional and statutory organisations. A series of brief presentations was given on each occasion, followed by structured discussion and debate. The appendix lists those who attended each meeting. The consultations aimed to:

- Examine the nature and consequences of youth homelessness.
- Consider the kinds of HIV/AIDS education that homeless young people might need.
- Identify appropriate strategies by which relevant HIV/AIDS education might be provided.
- Provide a forum for the exchange of views between different workers and different organisations.
- Produce a document detailing the issues discussed and any recommendations reached.

This report contains summaries of key presentations given at each meeting, as well as a resumé of the main points arising in plenary sessions. Its purpose is to stimulate further discussion and debate. The views it contains are those of consultation participants alone and should not be construed as those of the Health Education Authority or Goldsmiths' College, University of London.

Following the meetings, a draft document was produced detailing the issues discussed and conclusions reached. This was circulated, along with a brief questionnaire, to many of the organisations and individuals it had not been possible to invite to the consultations. Responses to the questionnaire are included in Chapter 10. They help to identify a growing consensus about what needs to be done and the relative responsibility of different organisations and agencies.

References

Centrepoint (1989) *Hungry and Homeless – A Sign of the Times*. London, Centrepoint Soho.

WHO (1990) Final Report from a Workshop on AIDS Education for the Hard to Reach. Copenhagen, WHO.

Young Homelessness Group (1990) *Young Homelessness – A National Scandal*. London, Young Homelessness Group.

CHAPTER ONE

Young People, Homelessness and HIV/AIDS

Peter Aggleton and Ian Warwick

By the end of June 1991, there had been 27 reported cases of AIDS and 530 reported cases of HIV infection amongst young people aged 15–19 in the UK; and 229 reported cases of AIDS and 2672 reported cases of HIV infection amongst those aged 20–24 (PHLS, 1991). Five per cent of all reported cases of AIDS and 20% of reported cases of HIV infection are therefore amongst those aged 15–24. Overall statistics like these conceal important sex differences and regional variations. For example, while almost 40% of the reported cases of HIV infection amongst women are in the 15–24 age group, this is true of only 19% of cases in men. The majority of new cases of infection continue to be reported in three of the four Thames health regions.

About 50% of young people in Britain will have experienced penetrative sex by the time they are aged 16. Of these, just over a quarter are likely to have had between two and three partners in the last twelve months, and about 10% will have had more than four partners. While 77% of 16-year-olds report using a condom at last intercourse, less than 50% of 19-year-olds are likely to have done so, demonstrating that condom use declines with age (HEA, 1992). In heterosexual relationships, the desire to avoid pregnancy rather than STDs continues to be the major factor influencing the kind of protection young people use (HEA, 1992).

While the media and popular opinion would sometimes have us believe that substantial numbers of young people use illicit drugs, hard data are more difficult to come by. Data are lacking too on the extent to which young people are involved in prostitution, although it seems plausible to suggest that lack of a job, lack of money and homelessness may predispose some to undertake this kind of work. In the report that follows, individual accounts provide testimony to this possibility and document some of the possible consequences for the health and well-being of young people involved in sex work.

The nature of youth homelessness

Leaving home is a natural and expected process in a culture which expects young people to live 'independently' once they become adults. This point cannot be stressed strongly enough. As a recent report says:

> Once they leave school (young people) are expected to make their own way in the world, get jobs, go to college, stand on their own feet, stop relying on their parents. All these things are seen as desirable in a young person, who should travel in search of employment and show initiative.
> (Young Homelessness Group, 1990)

Young people's hopes for the future differ little from those of others. Most people want somewhere secure to live, with a job which provides enough income for independent living, and it is in order to find this that the majority of young people leave home, sometimes travelling to those parts of the country where they believe prospects may be better. Whilst the majority of young people leave home because they want to, others may do so because of overcrowding, poverty, family arguments or other pressures. Some of these young people may need initial support, having left home before they felt ready to do so. Others may need this support in order to come to terms with physical, mental and sexual abuse.

But why, having left home, do some young people become homeless? There are no simple answers to this question; responses differ according to the perspective adopted. One popular view is that homelessness arises because of young people's unwillingness to find suitable accommodation. Another suggests that they may lack the skills whereby to do so. Yet another suggests that the real issue is housing, or lack of it.

Opinions differ as to the adequacy of each of these explanations, but of some things we can be certain. Low wages and lower rates of Income Support and Housing Benefit seriously disadvantage young people in the housing market. The supply of private rented accommodation has consistently declined over the last thirty years, local authority housing and temporary accommodation are in short supply, and home ownership is out of the reach of those who are unemployed or on low wages. Unlike homeless families, homeless single people have no right to council housing unless they can demonstrate through their 'vulnerability' that they have a priority need; and direct and indirect discrimination against those who are young, and who may therefore be perceived as unreliable by landlords, contributes to the problem (Young Homelessness Group, 1990; Agenda, 1990).

In the pages that follow, consultation participants voice their opinions about these and other issues. They do so drawing upon personal and professional experience working with homeless young people. If there is inconsistency in what follows, this is a reflection of the complexity of the problem and of the existence of differing perspectives on what needs to be done. As we will see, however, there are some points of agreement, and these help to establish an agenda for action.

Young people and HIV/AIDS education

Young people are often identified as a key group in relation to HIV/AIDS education, and several initiatives have now taken place both in and out of school to meet their needs. Nationally, the Health Education Authority (HEA) has co-ordinated a number of press, press and television and press and radio campaigns to maintain levels of awareness and to create and maintain a socially supportive climate for HIV/AIDS education in general. As part of this work, the specialist youth press has been used to disseminate information about HIV and AIDS.

Teachers in schools have been provided with inservice training by advisers and advisory teachers with responsibility for health education (national funding for these posts ceases in March 1993 and the future of such support is uncertain), as well as by the dissemination of the HEA's resources *Teaching about HIV and AIDS* and *Learning about AIDS*. The Department of Education and Science (DES) has produced a video resource package for use in secondary schools entitled *Your Choice for Life*, as well as booklets of guidance for teachers and those working in the youth service.

Youth and community workers and youth trainers have been provided with support via training resources such as: *AIDS: Working with Young People* published by the AIDS Education and Research Trust (AVERT), and the HEA has funded a number of community youth projects to examine different ways in which peer-led education can be used to meet young people's needs. A series of consultations organised jointly by the National AIDS Trust (NAT) and the HEA have provided young people with the opportunity to examine their awareness of issues relating to HIV/AIDS and to discuss different educational strategies.

A range of teaching packs produced by the HEA and other organisations contain material on HIV and AIDS within the context of more general work on health education or on personal and social relationships. *Health and Self – health education in the secondary school* is a completely revised and redesigned second edition of *Health education 13–18*. The resource provides a comprehensive framework for health education in the 1990s and includes an updated edition of *Teaching about HIV and AIDS* (co-published with Forbes Publications, £54.95, ISBN 0 901762 85 7). A revised edition of the HEA's *Health Action Pack*, a pack of health education material for use with 16–19-year-olds, is due in Spring 1993. The pack will contain substantially more material on HIV/AIDS and sexual health than the previous edition.

Strategies such as those described above are, however, unlikely to meet the needs of those young people who are not in school and who lack access to out-of-school provision such as youth clubs and youth organisations. Cut off from most of the channels conventionally used to communicate health education messages, they may be more vulnerable than others at the present time, and special provision may need to be made to meet their needs. Homeless young people constitute one such group, especially those living on the streets of major cities with little access to established systems of communication and health networks.

The three consultations summarised in this book provided an opportunity to consider some of the available educational options for work of this kind. Participants described some of the different ways in which young people could be reached through community-based youth projects. Most agreed that education on HIV and AIDS should be linked to other activities which promote health and well-being. All agreed that young people without homes are seriously disadvantaged when it comes to access to existing services and facilities. If no easy answers are identified, this is a consequence of the multi-faceted nature of the problem. Effective solutions are likely to require intervention at several different levels – economically, in the labour and housing markets; socially and culturally, to ensure that appropriate educational and communicative strategies are used; and, interpersonally, to ensure that the messages adults give and the support they offer are acceptable to young people themselves.

References

Agenda (1990) Homelessness, *Agenda*, 2, 1–15.

Health Education Authority (1992) *Today's Young Adults: 16–19-year-olds look at diet, alcohol, smoking, drugs and sexual behaviour*. London, Health Education Authority.

PHLS (1991) Statistics supplied by the Public Health Laboratory Service AIDS Centre, Colindale.

Young Homelessness Group (1990) *Young Homelessness – A National Scandal*. London, Young Homelessness Group.

CHAPTER TWO

Young Homeless People: Key Issues

Una Barry

This chapter discusses some of the key issues that affect homeless young people, particularly those visible in the West End of London today. The information is derived from the experience of Centrepoint Soho, a frontline organisation catering for the needs of homeless young people, and providing a spectrum of accommodation for different groups.

Centrepoint Soho currently offers four types of accommodation (Figure 1). The first is direct-access short-term accommodation which takes young people off the streets and attempts to prevent homeless young people becoming 'streetwise' or sleeping rough. The project operates two permanent shelters, one for the newly homeless and one for the long-term homeless. About 1400 young people are seen in the shelters each year, 60–70% of whom come from outside London. There has been a significant increase in young women and young people from minority ethnic communities using these shelters in the last year.

Hostel accommodation provides specific support and medium-term accommodation for three months to over a year, in order that young people can learn and develop skills for independence.

Semi-supported bedsits are the third type of accommodation offered by Centrepoint Soho. Here young people can learn to be independent and good tenants with the minimum of support. Finally, there is permanent move-on accommodation providing affordable and completely independent living for the young people concerned.

Why young people become homeless

Leaving home is usually a part of growing up – an entirely desirable and natural process. Sometimes, however, it can be a response to an intolerable situation or to the need to leave. Figure 2 lists the main reasons why young people in contact with Centrepoint Soho left home.

The data show that in 1989 more young people left home because of

Figure 1   **Types of accommodation offered by Centrepoint Soho**

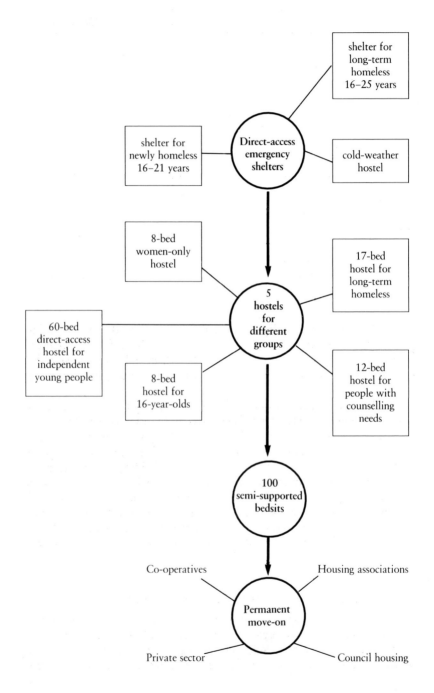

Figure 2   *Main reason for leaving last settled home (% of respondents)*

	1989 Survey	1987 Survey
Push factors		
Told to leave/evicted	24	19
Arguments	20	11
Left Care	6	5
Violence	2	3
DSS Board Payments cut off	6	1
Couldn't afford rent	6	1
Problems in neighbourhood	8	0
Other push factors	10	4
Total push factors	82%	44%
Pull factors		
To look for job/job offer	16	43
Liked idea of London	4	3
Other pull factors	0	10
Total pull factors	20%	56%

'push' factors (because they had to) than because of the desire to look for a job or other more positive reasons. This is a rather different situation than pertained some two years previously, when 'pull' factors were the major reasons why the equivalent group of homeless young people came to London.

Of homeless young people surveyed in 1989, 41% had lived in a children's home and a further 16% had lived with foster parents (Figure 3).

Figure 3 also shows that in 1989 a much larger percentage of young people slept rough in London than two years earlier. These findings have significant implications in relation to the 1989 Children Act and the need to establish good working relationships between local authorities and voluntary organisations. There is considerable scope for statutory and voluntary agencies to work together to meet the needs of homeless young people, and we all have a responsibility to ensure that young people obtain the best possible service that is available to them, as well as the advice and support that is their right.

Problems facing young people leaving home

Young people need access to affordable housing, which is increasingly difficult to gain in the current economic climate. Young people aged 16 and 17 also need the right to obtain tenancies from local authorities and housing associations, but again have few options open to them. Young

Figure 3   Accommodation experienced during lifetime (% of respondents)

	1989 Survey	1987 Survey
Children's home	41	23
Foster parents	16	11
Relatives other than parents	63	44
Hostel	55	30
Bed and breakfast/lodgings	43	42
Sleeping rough	78	53
Squatting	49	18
Flatshare	29	15
Own tenancy	29	14
Other night shelter	22	13
Detention/youth custody centre	27	16
Probation/bail hostel	12	7
Psychiatric hospital	6	1
Other	10	0

people need employment and a reasonable wage in order to be able to pay for accommodation and food. Often homeless young people find themselves in the trap of having no job, no money and, therefore, being unable to gain access to accommodation. Without accommodation, they often find it extremely difficult to obtain a job. They are thus caught in a vicious circle of disadvantage from which it is hard to escape.

In situations of this kind it is not easy to access benefits. Young people may not know or understand the system, and some do not think they are even eligible for support. In particular, 16 and 17-year-olds have extreme difficulty in relation to benefit claims.

Effects of long-term homelessness

One of the most worrying aspects of youth homelessness in London is the risk of sexual exploitation. About a third of the young men and young women with whom Centrepoint Soho comes into contact have been approached to become involved in prostitution. Figure 4 identifies areas of need other than those linked to accommodation. Money and work, not surprisingly, feature as high priorities. What is, perhaps, surprising is the number of young people needing help with health and stress management.

This need is all too apparent, though, when visiting the two night shelters. In that used by those who are newly homeless, young people are still enthusiastic, want a job and a flat and have great hopes of the future. In the other shelter, which works with longer-term homeless young people, there is less enthusiasm and much cynicism about the future. Thirty-one

Figure 4   **Problems receiving attention or with which help was wanted**
(% of respondents)

	1989 Survey	1987 Survey
Health	12	10
Stress	22	6
Drugs	6	0
Drink	8	6
Gambling	6	16
Work	59	52
Money	84	44
Total (100%) respondents	49	50

per cent of young people who become homeless state that their health has got worse as a result.

Many homeless young people suffer assault and abuse which can lead to despair. Unemployed homeless young people often lose their pride and self-esteem and become disillusioned. They experience poverty which leads to malnutrition, depression and ill-health. All this leads to increased anxiety and depression, and young people lose their motivation and sense of hope.

Health promotion strategies

Prevention is better than cure, and the earlier young people become involved in health promotion activities, the better. These should include not only education on health issues, but life skills to help them to cope and survive. It is often difficult to provide adequate medical care to homeless young people because of their mobility and their inability to attend for regular treatment. Moreover, not all young people know how to seek relevant medical advice, and some may be nervous of doing so.

At Centrepoint Soho, we have developed several strategies to help with health issues. As much information as possible is made available to young people on an educational basis and they are also provided with guidance about where to go to get appropriate help. Secondly, links have been developed with relevant local agencies, some of whom are willing to bring their services directly to young people using Centrepoint's accommodation. There is good liaison with local hospitals, doctors and advice projects, and several of these encourage their workers to offer a satellite service in the night shelter. It is important, where possible, to take the services to young people and make them accessible to all.

A major consideration in relation to service provision is confidentiality. The services offered must be confidential in order to ensure that young people will use them. Homeless young people often meet with prejudice, ignorance and intolerance, and it is important that services do everything possible in order to avoid this happening.

Conclusions

For many young people, homelessness makes the transition into adulthood extremely difficult. By providing adequate financial support, the right to housing when homeless, access to services and policies to tackle discrimination and harassment, we can do much to improve the lot of these young people. Then their transition to adulthood can become a positive experience, and the 'golden age' of youth need not become a time of hardship, depression and despair.

References

Randall, Geoffrey (1987) *No way home*. London, Centrepoint Soho.

Randall, Geoffrey (1989) *Homeless and Hungry*. London, Centrepoint Soho.

CHAPTER THREE

What You Know or Where You Are? Housing and the Effectiveness of Health Promotion

Roz Pendlebury

One of the assumptions which runs throughout much discussion about health promotion among homeless people is that homelessness is somehow an inevitable aspect of our society. The concern in this chapter is to put housing back at the centre of any debate focusing on homelessness and health. I do this in order to encourage health educators and health promoters to consider how much easier their work might be with young people if those young people were housed.

Three key sets of issues will be addressed. First, some time will be spent examining the links between housing and health. Second, there will be an examination of some of the evidence about the factors which make a difference to young people in terms of adopting risk-reducing behaviours. Third, some suggestions will be made concerning appropriate strategies for health promotion within a housing context.

Health and housing

The public and policy makers alike are becoming increasingly concerned about the well-documented and visible rise in homelessness in late twentieth-century Britain, and this concern is fuelled by increasing evidence suggesting that homelessness is hazardous to health. However, this has led to a tendency to medicalise the whole issue of homelessness. While there are many real ways in which homelessness *is* a public health issue, health education and health promotion amongst homeless people is also a housing issue – the urgency of which may be compromised if the lack of a home is not recognised as a serious block to risk-reducing behaviour amongst many young people and tackled accordingly.

The idea that housing has a major impact on public health first arose in the nineteenth century. Florence Nightingale, for example, said, 'The connection between health and the dwellings of the population is one of the most important that exists'. Thus, in the earliest days of British public policy, health and housing issues were linked with a single ministry (the

Ministry of Health), and the earliest interventions in the housing system were made via the Public Health Acts of the late nineteenth century. Today, however, the Department of Health and the Department of the Environment are firmly separated. The Housing Acts of the 1980s are all designed to reduce local authority rented housing stock which substantially undermines the social role of housing policy; and recent community care legislation, whilst referring to the role of housing, makes no legislative demands on housing departments. The Department of the Environment draft circular on community care for housing authorities states: 'Developments in community care policy do not fundamentally alter the role of local housing authorities'. Perhaps the main point of contact between health and housing services today comes about through social services departments, but service integration is limited and homeless people (particularly homeless young people) remain at the margins of all three main service areas, where the blame is all too readily shifted from one service to another.

Research into homelessness during the late 1980s confirms that having no home means having little or no health care (see, for example, Stearn, 1987), and that this in turn increases a range of health risks from perinatal mortality to chronic disability. It is not unreasonable to extrapolate from this that access to health care also means access to health education and health promotion, and that the risk of unsafe behaviour should therefore be included in the list of health hazards arising from homelessness.

What is clear from available research is that these features can be seen as primarily health indicators of a housing problem. One of the main reasons why a growing proportion of young people becomes exposed to the unhealthy and demoralising environments we associate with homelessness is a decline in affordable housing. Four sets of factors contribute to rising levels of homelessness amongst low-income groups and have a particular impact upon those who are young – the continuing decline of the privately rented sector; the recent decline in local authority rented stock; the rising costs of home ownership; and (underlying all three) the growing socio-economic inequalities in British society as a whole.

There is an additional source of concern. However much the boundaries of the welfare state contract, there is little doubt that, in theory at least, homeless people with medical needs should have priority among those entitled to local authority housing. But, as recently noted by Shanks and Smith (1991), those who already have medical needs are those most likely to be selected out of housing on to the streets. The point being made here is a general one about the policy links between health education and health promotion and housing. Housing policy must bear as much responsibility as the medical and paramedical professions for securing the health and welfare of homeless people. If this kind of intersectoral collaboration does not occur, the gains in terms of actual risk reduction will of necessity be limited.

Research evidence

Research from around the world shows a clear relationship between homelessness and risk behaviour amongst young people. A recent comparative study in Chicago and New York, for example, found that:

> the use of multiple narcotic substances is directly related to the experience of homelessness – constant mobility, fatigue, poor nutrition, erratic sleeping and constant interaction with strangers . . . emotions related to the experience of homelessness are often 'medicated' through the rise of stimulant drugs.
>
> (Popkin et al., 1991)

Supporting evidence for such a claim comes from recent statements by Louis Jordan of Act Up New York, who explained at the 7th International Conference on AIDS in Florence that 'many people turn to drugs as a way of coping with living on the streets'.

This same study highlights some of the practical problems linked to the adoption of risk-reducing practices whilst living on the streets. Homelessness means having nowhere to keep clean needles or to use bleach; it carries the risk of arrest for possessing injecting equipment; it makes injecting drug users more dependent on shooting galleries; and the likelihood of being arrested for soliciting makes carrying condoms a hazard.

Recent studies of the HIV/AIDS health related behaviour of homeless young people in the Phillipines suggests that, whilst knowledge levels may be high, only 10% of homeless 15–18-year-olds practise safer sex and adopt safer drug-use behaviours. When questioned about this, respondents showed low self-esteem, perceiving themselves as having little or no control over their situation. Many believed that they already had HIV, and said that everyone had to die sometime and that anyway they had very little to live for. What it is important to note, however, is that over the period of the study, those who achieved a significant improvement in their environment were more likely to adopt risk-reducing behaviours. Available research therefore clearly demonstrates that the emotional and practical problems of homelessness inhibit risk-reducing behaviours. It also suggests that material improvements in the environment may be as, if not more, important than information in promoting risk reduction.

HIV/AIDS health promotion strategies

Of course, housing is not the only answer. The present government's recent homelessness initiative has provided £80 million to be spent primarily by the voluntary sector on housing homeless people. This has raised important issues for voluntary organisations more used to campaigning for funding than receiving and spending it. As the director of the Homeless Network said recently:

We have had to re-examine our own rhetoric and what we mean by it. It has been all too easy to say that what homeless people need are houses: when confronted with flats and front-door keys, we need to admit that, like the rest of us, many homeless people need much more than that.

We need also to acknowledge the different meanings of different environments for the people who live in them. It is not uncommon for young people to practise safer sex in a hostel because it is a transitory setting, but revert to unsafe sex in the 'safety' of their own home. Homeless people as a group often define their needs in ways which conflict with institutional expectations, and therefore require additional outreach assistance which is seldom available.

In order, therefore, to offer an effective health promotion service to homeless young people, we must provide it on their own terms. Key elements within such an approach include providing a comprehensive programme of training for hostel workers on how to raise with residents and respond to issues related to HIV. Additionally, we need to explore how peer education can be used in medium and long-stay hostels where there is a stable client group. A particularly crucial time for health promotion activity is when young people are making the transition from a relatively unstable to a stable situation. This kind of work will involve educators, hostel workers and residents collaborating to develop an appropriate service.

We also have to understand that as educators we will be limited if we are unable to persuade the housing sector to acknowledge the health risks of homelessness. We must recognise the incredible strain that homelessness places on people, and we must fight for housing as a health promotion strategy – which is one of its traditional, though recently neglected roles in the British welfare state.

References

Popkin *et al.* (1991) Homelessness and Risk Behaviours amongst IVDUS in Chicago and New York. Paper presented at the 7th International Conference on AIDS, Florence.

Shanks, N. J. and Smith, S. J. (1991) Public Policy and the Health of Homeless People, *Policy and Politics*.

Stearn, J. (1987) No Home, No Health Care, *Roof*, May/June, 16–19.

CHAPTER FOUR

AIDS and Homelessness

Trevor Smith

HIV infection and AIDS are not among the top priorities of people who are homeless and sleeping on the streets. Their priorities are the immediate realities of needing shelter for the night and, in the long term, a home of their own; obtaining a hot drink and food; the hope of securing a job; in some instances coping with psychological problems; and the desire for companionship with other people. Faced with such harsh realities, for them HIV and AIDS can be a peripheral issue. Even for homeless people housed in hotels, bedsits, hostels and squats, the priorities do not necessarily radically change.

It can be salutary to remind ourselves that the vast majority of homeless people are not sleeping on the streets – they are housed in hotels, bedsits, hostels and squats. The media focuses on people sleeping on the streets because they are visible, easily filmed and photographed, and more dramatic, but it requires sound social research to highlight the far larger numbers of homeless people elsewhere. In 1988 the Salvation Army asked the University of Surrey to undertake a study which would 'generate the research basis from which co-operation on a strategic plan of the provisions necessary for homeless people in London, at present and in the foreseeable future, may be developed'. *Faces of Homelessness* is the name of the report published following this study. It highlights the diversity of homelessness within London, which is reflected in other parts of the country.

In 1989 there were at least 75 000 homeless people in London. Two thousand were sleeping on the streets, 18 000 were in hostels, 30 000 in squats and 25 000 in hotels. The report states that:

the development of an integrated system of hostel care would facilitate the flow-through of people from the street to settled accommodation. There is little value in concentrating entirely on the homeless person's basic need for a roof over his or her head. It is of more value to create a system whereby people move through co-ordinated stages to permanent accommodation.

Of those who are homeless, 64% are under the age of 39 – a 10% increase on ten years ago – and 73% of those squatting are under the age of 29. Seventy-one per cent of homeless people are single and 19% are women, housed mainly in hostels, squats and hotels. Of those accommodated in hotels, there are three times more women than men. Many are single-parent families. Twenty per cent of those in hotel accommodation are Black or Asian. Ninety-two per cent of the hotel residents are unemployed, and many are mothers with young children, with access to few if any childcare facilities.

Overall, 29% of homeless people in London are in some form of employment, as are over a third of those living on the street. On the Salvation Army's nightly soup run to the homeless on the streets of London, it is possible to meet those who are employed, some of whom may be trying to keep their overheads down by sleeping rough, and others who may be sending money to family and relatives elsewhere in the country. There is a high level of mental and emotional stress amongst those who are homeless, with those who are employed having less stress than the unemployed or those who are invalid or ill. The younger age groups have higher levels of stress than those who are older.

There is a sense of community amongst those who are homeless. The members of one group sleeping rough on the street may have a sense of camaraderie, of community, which they value. For those sleeping in ones and twos in shop doorways, this sense of community is diminished. And for that lone person sleeping under the bridge over the canal, a sense of community is negligible. And does that single-parent family in a bedsit or a hotel have any greater sense of community? For such a person, the sense of isolation, the lack of community, can be all the more acute.

HIV and AIDS

Against this background are set the challenges linked to HIV and AIDS. In responding to these, two things need to be considered – education and practical care. With regard to education, efforts must be made to increase the level of awareness amongst those who are homeless. Effective HIV/AIDS education will be that which not only makes its impact upon the immediate present, but influences future behaviour when, it is hoped, the homeless are able to establish themselves in permanent accommodation.

With regard to practical care, special attention needs to be given to the requirements of homeless people who have HIV or AIDS, especially those accommodated in hotels and bedsits, whose sense of community may be even less than those resident in squats or as a group sleeping rough on the streets.

In providing such education and practical care, begin first with the identified needs of those homeless people with whom you are already, or intend to be in the future, most closely associated. In the case of the Salvation Army, for example, this includes people within hostels and those contacted during the course of late-night soup runs and midnight patrol work. Having identified the community with which you wish to work, seek to involve representatives of that community in consultations prior to making a plan of action. Then implement and evaluate this plan.

But the real challenge lies in finding the political will to move beyond crisis management to effect an upgrading in the national housing stock, and the further development of housing association schemes, so that homelessness becomes much reduced. Education and practical care will be more effective if not only the people sleeping on the streets, but also the far greater number of the hidden homeless, are given hope that they may speedily progress to permanent accommodation of their own.

CHAPTER FIVE

Young People, Homelessness and Drug Use

Ailsa Duncan

In December 1989, work began within West Berkshire Health Authority to examine the health promotion needs of homeless young people. The aim was to examine their perspectives and to identify the kinds of local provision that might usefully be made. It was felt that it was better to do this than to rely on stereotypes and presuppositions about homeless young people, which might have no bearing upon reality locally. During this early work the place of focus was Reading, where there had been a recent increase in the number of young people presenting themselves to the local authority as homeless. Many of these were young single women with children and childcare responsibilities.

This local needs analysis led to the identification of three different categories of homeless young people. First, there were those who were transient or had been so in the past, perhaps through participation in one of those 'convoys' passing by Reading. Then there were those in receipt of 'community care'. Many of these individuals had been discharged from hospitals offering medium to long-term mental care. Their average age was older than that of people falling into the other two groups. Finally, there were older homeless people, many of whom had been living rough and on the streets for some time.

Having identified these different groups, the decision was made to begin work. A three-pronged strategy was adopted. This involved getting to know people, their situation and their awareness of services available locally. In order to do this, specific sites were targeted. Often these were squats within Reading, but sometimes they were open-air settings where homeless young people congregated. Project workers provided information on a wide range of health and social welfare issues, including housing, the availability of relevant health services, and welfare rights. In addition, material benefits such as warm clothing and items to meet household needs were sometimes provided. As part of this work, clean injecting equipment was offered when necessary. By using this kind of holistic approach, the initiative aimed to cater for a range of needs. This strategy is in contrast to some other initiatives, where the emphasis has been upon the provision of syringes and needles, and perhaps condoms, in the absence of parallel interventions to ameliorate the effects of homelessness itself.

By examining the economic, cultural and political issues to do with homelessness, and by aiming to offer an integrated response, the project won the respect of many of those with whom it came into contact. It also enhanced awareness locally of the reality of homelessness as an issue affecting some young people. High on the agendas of those with whom workers came into contact was information concerning legal and welfare rights, how best to access health care services, both general and more specialised, and how to go about obtaining housing. It is perhaps not surprising, therefore, that HIV/AIDS was not a major concern. Our experience suggests that for sizeable numbers of homeless young people, focused work on risk reduction can only take place once a range of other needs have been met. This poses problems for those who seek quick and easy solutions in their work for homeless young people since it suggests that intervention strategies must be multi-faceted. Attempts to normalise the experience of those who are young and homeless require special resources and effective intersectoral collaboration.

CHAPTER SIX

Meeting the Health Care Needs of Homeless Young People

Suzie Daniels

It is often suggested that HIV/AIDS education should take place as part of a broader programme which addresses a wide range of health related concerns. This may be particularly pertinent when meeting the needs of homeless young people. This chapter describes a local project in Nottingham set up to provide health care advice and support to young people out of school. It discusses the implications of such an approach for activities involving homeless young people.

In April 1987, in response to the large number of unplanned pregnancies and also to government directives advocating the provision of specific health services for young people, a Teenage Clinic was opened in Nottingham offering a two-hour session each week. The clinic was originally intended to provide support in relation to a wide range of health issues facing young people – from relationship problems, to worries about acne, to contraceptive needs. Since its inception, the clinic has been extensively used and three sessions per week are now offered, with over 30 young people being seen at each of these. The 'grapevine' has, however, turned this resource into a clinic providing contraceptive advice – over 96% of young people attend for this, pregnancy testing or abortion referral.

When the clinic opened, I was employed to co-ordinate service provision and to examine the broader sexual health needs of young people. It became of increasing concern that, while the service was being extensively used, it seemed largely to meet the needs of well-motivated, white, middle-class young women. Only 1% of attenders were young men. There was a danger of the clinic becoming an 'in and out' facility and the possibility of expanding the service seemed limited.

In April 1989, the joint-planning team for children convened a working group on meeting the health care needs of young people. This group comprised workers from a broad spectrum of agencies, including social services, education, youth services, health services and the voluntary sector, including Childline, Hostels Liaison and the Race Equality Council. The group looked at the overall health care needs of young people, risk-taking and the options open for support. The six-month consultative process led to the production of a written report which documents some of the issues and concerns.

1. 'Falling in love', sexual learning and occasional experimentation are all a part of growing up. They can be exciting and fulfilling but also involve the risk of unplanned pregnancy and sexually transmitted diseases, including cervical cancer and HIV infection. Abuse and exploitation, too, can sometimes be a part of early sexual experience. In relation to these and other issues it is important particularly to emphasise the gender-specific needs of young women. Often women have little choice or control over whether they have sexual relationships, and almost always the relationships themselves are unequal. Knowing about safer sex is one thing but being able to practise it is another. Young women require power and skills which many of us as adults are still learning how to acquire.

2. Recent government legislation has created a difficult context for sex education, and makes it hard for young people to access relevant health and social services. Section 28 of the 1988 Local Government Act has resulted in much confusion and fear, and it is young people who suffer in the end.

3. Alcohol and other drugs can easily be misused, leading to long-term problems of addiction. Alcohol poses perhaps the biggest drug risk because it is such an accepted part of our lives.

4. The stresses of growing up can be immense. Family relationships change, and often become strained, or break down. There are many difficulties in building and maintaining sexual relationships. Young people often feel powerless in defining their own lives.

5. Homelessness, poverty, unemployment and abusive homes or environments can contribute to depression and low self-esteem. Feeling positive about oneself, and having high self-esteem is essential for risk reduction and enhanced health.

6. Finally, there are cross-cultural needs to consider. When providing for young people, we are not dealing with an homogeneous group. The realities of living in

multiracial Britain must be addressed, as well as the gender-specific needs of young women and young men, the needs of young people with disabilities, and the needs of gay and lesbian youth.

Young people and homelessness

Nottingham is not unique in seeing a growing population of homeless young people during the 1980s. In 1988, Nottingham University, in conjunction with the voluntary sector, initiated a survey on 'Homeless Young People in Nottingham'. Over a six-month period it was found that 1800 homeless people had approached the 21 housing agencies in the city. Of these, 40% were under the age of 25, and 25% were under the age of 18. A worrying finding from the survey was the marked number of homeless young women in the 16–18 age group. The study also showed that, in terms of the action likely to be taken by agencies, young women were less likely to be housed permanently and more likely to be offered advice and temporary assistance. The number of direct-access emergency accommodation beds currently available for young women in the city is two!

The same survey found that the inability or unwillingness of friends, relatives or immediate family to continue to accommodate a young person was the single most common reason given for homelessness. There are many young people 'dossing' from one friend's house to the next, having been made to leave their own home or having left institutionalised care.

The joint-planning team working group looked at all of these issues and examined a number of models of care which might meet these wide-ranging needs. Our aim was to adopt an holistic approach. Using World Health Organisation recommendations as our starting point, we aimed to develop this kind of provision by involving the young people themselves, adopting an intersectoral approach and being as comprehensive as possible. We believed that an approach limited to warnings about risk factors and specific models of behavioural change was inadequate for the promotion of healthier lifestyles. Instead, we hope to develop comprehensive ways by which to support young people both individually and collectively.

The model which most appealed to us derived from work at a comprehensive, health/youth centre in New York called The Door. The Door opened in 1972 with the goal of enabling inner-city teenagers to lay the foundation upon which to build a healthy, productive and meaningful life. For 20 years it has offered a comprehensive programme of events and services for young people – from primary health care to drama and literacy groups. In 1990, the centre provided more than 12 000 free meals to young people in New York City as one of the 30 co-ordinated services and programmes available from their large Lower West Side building. Central to the project's philosophy is the notion of integration. The belief is that the needs of young people, particularly those who are most vulnerable, are best met by an approach which does not compartmentalise them but deals with them holistically. The aim is to involve young people actively in setting goals and providing services. In this way feelings of powerlessness can be challenged and self-esteem raised.

Following this background work, the working group proposed the establishment of an independent, full-time young people's health care centre in Nottingham. This centre would aim to meet the needs of those young people with limited access to existing services. Priority would be given to service provision for homeless youth, young people in care or just leaving care, young people with disabilities, minority groups including gay and lesbian youth as well as those from minority ethnic communities, young mothers, young people with experiences of abuse within the family, and young unemployed people. The hope was to create a large, drop-in centre which could meet the physical, psychological, emotional and spiritual needs of young people and prevent the occurrence of avoidable health-related problems. The project would be independent, aiming over time to become a charity, thereby easing the access of young people alienated from statutory agencies.

In May 1991, a meeting was held with senior officers from Nottingham Health Authority, Nottinghamshire County Council, Nottingham City Council and the voluntary sector to undertake further planning. Funding was provided for an 18-month development post linked to the evaluation of the existing young people's health clinic.

The project's intentions derive from the view that to approach a homeless young person, particularly a young woman, and try to get her or him to look at their HIV risk without first addressing other more immediate needs, will be counter-productive. Accordingly, the centre will provide a programme of activities and events identified as relevant by young people themselves. Services available will include crisis intervention for those living on the streets. Such intervention will include referral to the homelessness office of the local authority as well as the provision of immediate, short-term accommodation. There will also be a café offering cheap, hot and nutritious meals; a social space to meet in; crèche provision for young parents; and specific clinical sessions for counselling, sexual health and primary health care. A wide range of other activities will be available, including self-defence, drama, music, sport and leisure activities, arts and crafts.

Outreach work will be integral to the work of the centre, and the sooner this begins the more the project will be able effectively to reflect the needs of potential and long-term users. Particular emphasis will be put on work with those who are homeless and there will be dedicated facilities such as a laundry, lockers and showers specifically for such individuals.

Negotiations are currently underway to secure appropriate premises in the city centre. There is already solid revenue support from the county council and contracts are being established with the health authority, alongside fundraising from trusts and charitable foundations. Intersectoral co-operation is essential if the project is to reflect a genuinely integrated approach to care. Ultimately the centre will seek charitable status, which is particularly important in service provision for young people, many of whom may be wary of statutory agencies. Evaluation will be in-built. Many of the strategies employed are relatively new and we will need to assess carefully how far they are able to meet the needs of homeless young people in Nottingham.

CHAPTER SEVEN

HIV/AIDS Health Promotion with Street-based Men who have Sex with Men

Barbara Gibson

Streetwise Youth is a charity which offers support, education and non-judgemental counselling to young men selling sex, most of whom are homeless. The homeless people the project works with may be sleeping rough, staying with friends temporarily, staying with a punter (a man or woman who buys sex), or staying in a night shelter, short-stay hostel or a squat. In order to carry out its work, Streetwise Youth has actively recruited staff from different cultural backgrounds. There are three project workers, a team leader responsible for the project's day-centre, an outreach team leader, outreach workers, an administrator, an administrative assistant, an executive director and a management committee.

Clients usually hear about the project through word of mouth. When members first arrive at the day-centre they are encouraged to identify their problems and these are used as the starting point for subsequent work. Those who use the project in this way are known as 'members'. The project is generally perceived as attractive since it responds to practical needs. Washing facilities are provided as well as a free meal and drinks. Young men can use the day-centre to 'crash out' and get off the streets. Short and longer-stay accommodation can sometimes be found in hostels, and housing associations can sometimes offer supportive shared housing. Some of these agencies specialise in providing for vulnerable young people and have effective equal-opportunities policies. Appropriate accommodation is, however, in short supply and there may be several applicants for one vacancy. Sometimes members give up on project workers after waiting for weeks or even months.

Clients' needs

In order to be able to educate the homeless young people with whom Streetwise Youth comes into contact, it is essential to gain their trust, speak their language, and empathise with their lifestyles and the circumstances which led them to be involved in sex work. Homeless young people live with uncertainty from day to day. They often arrive at the day-centre exhausted due to lack of sleep, and many use recreational drugs and alcohol to block out the realities of their current existence as well as the traumas of the past. An inability to claim social security benefits causes problems. It is necessary, for example, for 16 and 17-year-olds first to prove that they are unable to return home, and social security officers often wish to make contact with parents to confirm that this is the case. Some members feel that if they sign on they will be forced to undertake youth training – the system is complicated and involves appointments which those who are homeless may find they are unable to keep. Others think that the police will catch up with them if they sign on, and as a result see no financial alternative but to sell sex or beg in order to survive.

The day-centre provides the first opportunity for many of the young men to talk about the sexual activities they feel they are forced to do. For example, one member arrived very distressed – on the one hand he was bragging about the great place he was staying in, but then he revealed the slash marks on his back where he had allowed himself to be continuously whipped. Members often express their feelings of anger, disgust and frustration, sometimes verbally and more rarely in the form of violence. Often attempts are made to 'test' project workers before trust is established.

Many homeless young people feel at the end of their tether and that there is no way out of what they are doing. Their self-esteem and self-worth may be low, and there is little motivation to bother to do anything. In this kind of situation HIV is just another problem amongst many others. Society seems to have conditioned many of the homeless young men we work with to think that they are outcasts and that they have AIDS *because* they are rentboys, regardless of the activities they do. Some even see having AIDS as an interesting release in their life. One member recently said that a diagnosis would punish his parents for the way they had treated him.

Many are desperate for love and companionship, and use sex as a means of getting it. Relationships can become intense very quickly and because condoms may be seen as barriers to love their use may sometimes be abandoned. Some deny that their female partners could potentially infect them, even though they know women who are already infected. Some have a strong need to have children – many do have children. One member who sees himself as gay recently confided that he was having a sexual relationship with a girl, and in spite of her knowing his HIV status she refused to allow him to use a condom. In his desperation, he put her on the telephone, asking me to explain the risks, but to no avail.

The project continually tries to build morale by challenging the put-down statements members constantly make about themselves. Efforts are made to encourage greater assertiveness, using group work to help improve social skills.

HIV/AIDS education

In order to educate the homeless young people with whom Streetwise Youth comes into contact, several different but complementary approaches should be adopted. These include:

- One-to-one counselling in a 'safe' environment and as part of outreach work.
- Peer counselling.
- Awareness raising through group discussions and games.
- Provision of easily accessible safer-sex information, for example, in comic or booklet form.
- Easy access to condoms, lubricant and clean needles and syringes, especially at night.
- A dedicated telephone helpline.
- Education for punters.

Streetwise Youth aims to offer each member a one-to-one, face-to-face session on HIV/AIDS soon after he has first attended the project and when it is felt a rapport has been established. The purpose of this session is to provide information on HIV and STDs and to dispel myths. It also offers an opportunity to give skills training around negotiating for safer sex and to alert members to potentially dangerous situations. Condom demonstrations are part of this work and include showing how to put them on with the mouth. Attention is also given to ways of eroticising safer sex so that alternatives can be offered to punters or friends who may ask for an activity members do not wish to do, receptive anal sex for example.

This one-to-one session provides an opportunity to have questions answered and allows members to express their feelings. Efforts are made to encourage the young men to do most of the talking, and it is usually as part of this work that the identification of current concerns takes place. We use appropriate street language where necessary to break the ice. Alternatives to high-risk activities are talked about in order to alert members to what they may be asked to do, and to prepare them more adequately to deal with this kind of situation. One-to-one sessions usually take about an hour and a half. They can be very bonding, and a lot of trust can develop between the counsellor and her or his clients. This trust is important if members are to return later to clarify things they were not sure about and to discuss their problems.

A pilot questionnaire is used to assess knowledge levels prior to the one-to-one session and this reveals much about existing sources of information, current sexual activities and HIV/AIDS-related risk. Efforts are made to evaluate changes in this baseline knowledge at three-monthly intervals.

When carrying out HIV/AIDS education with homeless young people such as those that Streetwise Youth comes into contact with, it is important to make available suitable condoms and lubricants. These are freely available in the bathroom at the day-centre. Many homeless young people may have poor mouth hygiene, rendering them prone to mouth infections and ulcers. As a result they may be at greater risk of acquiring HIV through oral sex. Flavoured condoms are therefore also available.

It is essential to try to create an open and non-judgemental environment in the day-centre so that members feel free to talk about sex, sexuality and drug use. This helps to facilitate spontaneous discussion about HIV. Appropriately managed night shelters and hostels can also offer this liberating environment, as night-time is a particularly good time for people to get together and talk.

Outreach work

In order to make contact with as many homeless young people as possible, Streetwise Youth carries out outreach work in a number of locations in London, including main-line railway stations. Outreach workers hand out 'jamboree bags' which contain information about what is available for homeless young people. These are received eagerly and treated as presents – after all, no-one gives them things. They also contain condoms, including flavoured ones which often promote discussion, and small sachets of lubricant. Additional outreach workers are being taken on to enable the project to reach clients in bars and on the streets and in order to expand our services and explore new ways of making contact.

Project workers also support members by going with them to clinics or to court. We keep contact with them while they are in prison, and visit them in hospital. Streetwise Youth fills a gap by providing a service on a regular and consistent basis to those not accessed by mainstream provision. Many clients are suspicious of existing services, seeing them as unsafe, judgemental and discriminatory.

Future activities

An HIV/AIDS information cartoon booklet for young men selling sex is currently being developed. This will reflect typical daily scenarios and will use members' humour and language in order to promote safer sex. The aim is to produce a resource which will be comprehensible to those of a low reading age and with characters representative of the multicultural environment in which we work. It will address sexual activities (e.g. fisting and scat) which are not normally included in safer sex literature in Britain, and will give useful advice on how to negotiate for safer sex. It is hoped that this kind of material can be made available via outreach work as well as in the day-centre.

Although Streetwise Youth has a helpline to enable members to keep in touch, and to provide them with information about HIV/AIDS, it is not advertised widely because of lack of resources. The project is aware, however, that it is reaching some people under the age of 16, who are unable to use the facilities of the day-centre and who cannot be reached through street work. In order to meet some of their needs, a peer training programme is to be initiated. Many members say that their knowledge of HIV prior to attending Streetwise had been largely gained through friends. This is why a peer education approach may prove useful in reaching those who would not be likely to come into contact with our work in any other way. Additional benefits can accrue through enhancement of the peer educator's own self-esteem, confidence and life skills.

When members were asked recently to come up with a set of guidelines for HIV/AIDS education for homeless young people such as themselves, the following principles emerged.

1. This kind of education should be non-discriminatory and non-judgemental, and it should begin in schools from the age of 11 when some young people start to become sexually active. Teachers and schools have a responsibility though to create a safe environment for discussion.

2. Young people need more 'safe' places to go which are non-judgemental, non-discriminatory and accepting, and where they can talk about and get help with their problems. These should be places where they can meet their peers and talk freely about sex, drugs and HIV. They should be open night and day.

3. There should be mobile vans with health educators to cater specifically for young people's needs. These vans could provide coffee, soup, condoms and needles and be a source of entertainment, showing videos, both educational and otherwise.

4. Dedicated health care facilities are needed where homeless young people can go to see doctors, dentists and nurses. These need to be user-friendly environments open twenty-four hours a day. They should be accessible to people under the age of 16, who are at present driven underground.

5. Finally, HIV/AIDS education should promote safer sex as fun and natural.

Several obstacles remain when educating homeless young people about HIV/AIDS. At present it is hard to reach the under-16s as there is a legal responsibility to report them to social services, although the use of peer education could overcome this. Relationships between the police and homeless young people are often judgemental, discriminatory and lacking in understanding. The young homeless are frequently arrested. If they are stopped – which happens regularly – condoms are confiscated in the mistaken belief it will stop them having sex.

So, for HIV/AIDS education to be successful with this target group we need to create places where homeless young people can feel 'safe', and where they can talk freely about sex and drugs. Help with practical problems such as housing and employment should also be offered through these centres. Additional efforts should be made to reach homeless young people on the streets and in the places they frequent. Existing medical and social services should be reorientated to make them more available and easily accessible at all hours. Peer education approaches should be used to reach those who are otherwise inaccessible. Above all, sex should be promoted as acceptable and fun, and the age of consent for sex between men should be brought into line with that for sex between women and men.

CHAPTER EIGHT

HIV and STDs – Working with Street-based Men who have Sex with Men

David Tomlinson

As described in the previous chapter, Streetwise Youth is an organisation founded in 1985 to help destitute young men involved in prostitutional activity. It is a charity and provides a day-centre at a safe address where every day of the week, free of charge to those who use it, a hot meal can be obtained. There are also showering and laundry facilities and a young and enthusiastic project staff of both sexes and all sexual orientations, who aim to meet a wide range of demands, including housing needs, emotional support and counselling. A non-judgemental, tolerant and accepting environment is provided and is expected to be maintained by members (as those who use the centre are called) and project staff alike. There is an experienced HIV counsellor to disseminate information about safer sex, to promote the use of condoms and non-penetrative sex, and to provide pre- and post-test counselling to those who wish to be tested. This latter advice is provided in conjunction with the more formal counselling that health care professionals offer.

The project makes available a variety of condoms suitable for oral, vaginal and anal sex, as well as water-soluble lubricants. Plans are afoot to develop safer-sex literature with direct input from those using the centre, to ensure that this uses their language and addresses their concerns. An outreach team consisting of two workers is attached to Streetwise Youth to make contact with young men on the street who are not being accessed by other services, and to liaise with other outreach workers in London through the Streetworkers Alliance.

An afternoon medical clinic is offered by the project once a week, combining a basic general-practitioner type service with more specialised STD screening and counselling for sexual health. Funded by Parkside Health Authority and the Jefferies Research Trust, the service aims to cater for a variety of needs. Centre users who have a permanent address are encouraged to register with a local general practitioner.

Screening and counselling for STDs including HIV

While the facilities currently offered are far from ideal, there is a small private room for consultations and examination. Testing for STDs other than HIV is undertaken and priority is given to encouraging those who are not already immune to Hepatitis B to be vaccinated. Over the past two years, 52 young men have been tested for markers for Hepatitis B infection, and of these, 10 (19.2%) were surface or core antibody positive and therefore had natural immunity. The majority, if not all, had acquired the infection by sexual contact as there was no excess of reported past or current injecting drug use, blood-product exposure or reported acute Hepatitis contacts. None were persistently infected with Hepatitis B. The 42 young men (80.8%) were not immune to Hepatitis B; and of these 12 (28.6%) did not return for their test results and could not therefore be offered vaccination. Thirty did re-attend and 27 (90%) of these subsequently started the vaccination programme. This consists of three injections at four-weekly intervals. So far 16 (53.3%) have completed a full course of vaccination, and a further 11 have received at least one shot of vaccine. These figures compare favourably with those seen in the STD clinic at St Mary's Hospital, London, where more than half of men tested do not return for their results, and only a third complete the full course of vaccination.

HIV antibody testing

While tests for other STDs are performed if required, or if there are indications that they may be needed, the decision was made early on in the life of the project that HIV testing would not be performed as part of this work. It was felt that it was impossible to guarantee confidentiality in the day-centre. HIV testing is discussed and pre-test counselling given, and a subsequent appointment is made at St Mary's Hospital, London, where confidentiality can be maintained. By offering HIV antibody tests at St Mary's Hospital, we believe it is possible to distinguish those individuals who genuinely want to know their sero-status from those young men who may feel on impulse that it would be a good thing to do. It allows those who are tested to receive pre-test counselling at Streetwise Youth as well as by Health advisers at the clinic. Test results are given in a 'neutral' place, away from peer-group members, along with post-test counselling and referral to a clinical psychologist if further support is required. Twelve members have been tested for HIV and of these, 3 (25%) were HIV seropositive. All were offered access to relevant services and facilities at St Mary's Hospital, with myself acting as the point of contact.

'Paul'

While we should be careful not to infer too much from one case-history, the experiences of one regular user of the day-centre, Paul, are perhaps not untypical. An outgoing, cheerful young man of 19, Paul had lived in various squats and short-stay hostels as well as on the street for a year, being involved in street prostitution for most of this time. He was a regular attender at the project and was fully aware of safer-sex practices, having had extensive discussions with both the HIV/AIDS counsellor and myself. Condoms and lubricants were readily available from the bathroom cabinets and offices of Streetwise Youth. He was not immune to Hepatitis B and completed the full course of vaccination. A few months ago, however, he returned to the centre complaining of a sore throat, dry cough, fever and a rash. Clinically, the diagnosis was an acute seroconversion reaction to HIV. Once told that this was probably the case, he said that he had had unprotected anal sex with a paying partner some six weeks previously, a fact he had initially denied. The reason was purely financial – he had been evicted from his squat, had no money and was hungry. The offer of an extra £20 was a more immediate attraction than the fear of acquiring HIV.

This case demonstrates eloquently how HIV, AIDS and even general health concerns are often *irrelevant* in the daily struggle of homeless young people to survive. No matter how good our communication skills, no matter how relevant the safer-sex material, no matter how available are condoms and lubricant, the immediate and pressing need to feed and clothe oneself outweighs the potential threat of infection. The fundamental problems of homelessness, having no regular source of income, food, clothing and shelter, must be addressed *before* homeless young people can take responsibility for their health. The threat of an infection with a long latency and little immediate effect does not have the same impact on those who are homeless as it may have on other groups. Programmes of HIV/AIDS education for young people such as Paul must be offered alongside practical means of support which empower the individual to change his or her circumstances and thereby modify their risk behaviour. This requires effective intersectoral liaison between social services, voluntary organisations and health care providers.

CHAPTER NINE

Streetwork and Health Issues

Alan Baldwin and Pepe Roche

Youthlink, Birmingham, was established in 1987 as part of The Children's Society 'Young People under Pressure' initiative. Other projects under the scheme have been set up in London, Bournemouth, Newport, Manchester and Leeds. Youthlink offers a drop-in advice, counselling and support service from Monday to Friday, plus an extensive programme of streetwork. In 1990, 270 young people visited the drop-in centre, while the detached service saw 155 young people. The work of Youthlink is very much focused on young people at risk of exploitation and abuse.

In October 1989, West Birmingham Health Authority appointed an outreach worker to the project. His responsibility was to contact young people whose sexual behaviour or whose drug use could put them at increased risk of acquiring or transmitting HIV. The aim was to undertake work which would reduce this risk and improve the health and well-being of the young people concerned. This involves participation in streetwork with other members of the Youthlink team. Much of the work takes place in a small part of the Birmingham city centre which is a focus for male prostitutional activity. Other young people are drawn to this area, including young women who are on the fringes of prostitution, or who are the girlfriends of some of the young men involved.

Before this joint work could be undertaken, the initial problems involved in a statutory organisation (West Birmingham Health Authority) and a non-statutory organisation (The Children's Society) working in conjunction with one another had to be resolved. To this end, a joint confidentiality policy and a professional practice policy were drawn up and agreed to by both organisations.

Much of the work carried out takes place with young people who are mistrusting of adults, particularly those adults who are perceived as representing the establishment. This mistrust can be allayed by providing practical help and support. The majority of the young people are homeless, either by virtue of being absconders from local authority care (runaways or pushed-aways) or from home. Some are in short-stay hostel accommodation. Practical help and support often involves advocacy with local authorities, family and statutory organisations, such as social security, social services and probation, in an effort to locate more permanent and safe accommodation. Providing homeless young people with access to medical centres which are willing to offer them services is also important in gaining trust.

Youthlink's premises form a base from which outreach work can take place. A great deal of preparatory work has to be carried out with homeless young people before sensitive subjects such as sexual behaviour, drug misuse and HIV/AIDS can be addressed. In our experience, this involves talking about general health issues, as well as homelessness and unemployment, well before HIV/AIDS-specific education takes place. HIV/AIDS may not figure highly on the agendas of many of the young people with whom the project comes into contact, since the lack of a home and of employment constitutes a more important problem. An holistic approach, therefore, should be taken when raising awareness of issues relating to HIV/AIDS. Work has to begin with the problems homeless young people see themselves as having, and solutions found to those, before subjects such as safer sex can be talked about.

CHAPTER TEN

Perceptions of Need

Ian Warwick and Peter Aggleton

In the final stage of the consultation exercise documented here, a draft document detailing issues discussed at the consultation meeting, along with an accompanying questionnaire, enquiring about the HIV/AIDS education needs of homeless young people, was sent to 400 individuals and agencies engaged in work with young people. The items included in the questionnaire are listed at the end of this chapter. A covering letter invited workers to take time to read the document and complete the questionnaire.

Workers from a variety of agencies were sent this document and questionnaire, including those who had attended earlier consultations, those engaged in research with young people, District HIV Prevention Co-ordinators, health promotion officers with a responsibility for HIV/AIDS health promotion and/or work with young people, directors of public health, and members of voluntary and statutory organisations engaged in HIV/AIDS education and/or homelessness work with young people. Respondents were able to reply anonymously if they so wished. The aim of this exercise was to broaden the consultation process to include people who were unable to attend the earlier meetings, but who might nevertheless be interested in commenting on and making suggestions about this important area of work.

From the 81 replies received by the closing date for receipt of the questionnaires, it was clear that respondents were keen to include their own suggestions rather than comment specifically on the content of the consultative document. We drew their responses together, noting the themes most often referred to for each of the questions.

The views of respondents

Question 1

Respondents were asked what they believed are the major HIV/AIDS health promotion needs of homeless young people. The most frequent response ($n = 23$) pointed to a need for more information. This covered a range of areas, including general HIV/AIDS and health information as well as more specific topics such as welfare benefit rights, dietary advice and alcohol information. Two respondents stated that information should be easy to read. Nineteen responses identified the value of skills-based work to enhance homeless young people's self-esteem. Nineteen others suggested that support should be offered by detached or outreach workers or those working in drop-in centres. A further 19 responses highlighted the need for housing, and a final 19 stated that mainstream services should be made more accessible to homeless young people. Drop-in centres were seen as helpful in providing places where homeless young people can talk, access to services, and food. Access to condoms ($n = 16$) was felt to be important.

Question 2

The main way in which respondents believed local authorities could help was in the provision of some form of housing or shelter ($n = 44$). This covered long-term housing provision ($n = 27$), through to temporary or emergency hostels ($n = 9$) and supported accommodation ($n = 4$). Four respondents suggested that local authorities could help by co-ordinating inter-agency work. Key agencies mentioned were voluntary organisations ($n = 13$), health authorities ($n = 13$), the youth service ($n = 8$), schools ($n = 3$) and the police ($n = 3$). Fourteen respondents suggested that social services help should be more readily available, with 5 people specifically mentioning that residential care should be an important focus for work.

Question 3

Concerning the role of health authorities, 28 respondents suggested that joint action should be taken with local authorities and voluntary organisations. Nineteen respondents wanted to see health authorities taking more action in enabling homeless young people to have greater access to primary health care, and 6 respondents believed staff would need training in issues of homelessness to enable this to happen. The setting up of specific services was felt to be important by 19 respondents. Thirteen of these suggested outreach projects while 6 mentioned the need for drop-in centres. Seven respondents stated that health authorities should take the lead in assessing the needs of young people without homes. The same number wanted health authorities to provide more information about HIV infection and AIDS.

Question 4

Respondents were asked to consider the kinds of accommodation that would best meet homeless young people's HIV/AIDS health promotion needs. Regardless of whether short-term, medium-term or longer-term accommodation was considered most suitable, 39 responses suggested that worker-support was also needed – not solely related to HIV/AIDS education, but also covering areas such as dietary advice and life-skills training. Five respondents particularly stressed that while accommodation is needed, its availability should not be tied to HIV/AIDS health promotion.

Question 5

The most often suggested legislative change was that welfare benefit rules should be amended so that people between the ages of 16 and 17 would once more be eligible for state financial support ($N = 17$). Eight respondents suggested that being young and homeless should be sufficient to classify a person as 'vulnerable' under the Housing Act and so eligible for accommodation from a local authority. Enabling local authorities to use funds from council house sales to build homes was suggested by 7 respondents. Ten respondents suggested that no legislative changes were needed but that current funding levels should be increased or used more creatively, or that proper implementation of current legislation, such as the Children Act, was needed.

Question 6

Of those respondents who answered Question 6, all felt that changes in sex education in schools were needed. The changes most frequently mentioned related to staff, with 16 respondents stating that there should be a greater level of staff training in schools. Four respondents suggested that teachers of sex education should be those interested in it. Seven respondents felt it was important that outsiders came into school to help with sex education. Making sex education compulsory in every school was felt to be necessary by 14 respondents. Thirteen suggested that a spiral curriculum, in which specific topics are returned to on several occasions, be adopted.

Question 7

Collaborative training of workers to undertake HIV/AIDS education with homeless young people was favoured by 19 respondents. Five respondents, however, felt that training should be agency-specific. Seventeen suggested that it be experiential, covering values and feelings as well as actual factual concerns. Eight respondents stated that they would like to see training covering basic facts and information.

Question 8

Respondents were asked to consider how best to undertake HIV/AIDS work with young sex workers. It was overwhelmingly stated that this should take the form of detached or outreach work ($n=42$). Nine respondents suggested that peer education could be used, and 8 felt that drop-ins or meeting spaces could be utilised for HIV/AIDS education.

Question 9

Many respondents felt they were unable to comment on the specific kinds of outreach or detached work that would best meet the needs of homeless young people. Nine respondents, however, suggested that it should begin identifying what young people need. Others suggested that drop-in centres were needed ($n=4$), and that any service provided should not be easily identifiable with statutory bodies ($n=4$).

Question 10

The aspects of social and life-skills training that most respondents believed to be most necessary were those concerned with communication and self-image. Some training on budgeting ($n=5$) and welfare benefits ($n=5$) was also felt to be important.

Question 11

Again, many respondents felt unable to comment on other needs that young people without homes may have. Ten respondents suggested that their needs should first be directly assessed to find this out. Eight respondents felt that more peer education projects should be conducted. The use of mobile clinics, whereby services are taken to homeless young people, was felt by 6 respondents to be necessary.

Conclusion

Three main themes ran through respondents' suggestions. First, ways should be found of making current services more relevant to the needs of homeless young people. This may, for example, require staff training or making available a greater range of services within such places as hostels or drop-in centres. Second, services need to be brought to homeless young people. This could be done in the form of mobile health clinics, or by running detached or outreach projects. Finally, many respondents stressed the need to tackle homelessness as a priority, with 2 believing that the provision of homes should come before any HIV/AIDS health promotion work. The integration of HIV/AIDS health promotion with responses to housing, dietary, financial and employment needs will require sensitive planning and intervention if it is to be effective and credible, both with workers and homeless young people themselves.

List of questions asked of respondents as part of the broader consultation

1. What in your view are the major HIV/AIDS health promotion needs of homeless young people?

2. Do local authorities have a responsibility in relation to homeless young people's HIV/AIDS health promotion needs? If so, what do you feel they should do?

3. Do health authorities have a responsibility in relation to homeless young people's HIV/AIDS health promotion needs? If so, what do you feel they should do?

4. What kinds of short-, medium- and longer-term accommodation best meet homeless young people's HIV/AIDS health promotion needs?

5. Do you feel that legislative changes are necessary to provide more adequately for homeless young people's HIV/AIDS health promotion needs? If so, what kinds of changes are needed?

6. Are changes needed to ensure that sex education in schools takes place more effectively? If so, what kinds of changes would be helpful?

7. Do you feel that training is needed to prepare teachers, youth workers, housing workers, social workers and voluntary sector workers for their HIV/AIDS health promotion work with young people? If so, what form might this training take?

8. How best can we undertake HIV/AIDS-related health promotion with homeless young people involved in prostitution and sex work?

9. What kinds of outreach and detached work best meet homeless young people's HIV/AIDS health promotion needs?

10. Does social and life-skills training have a role to play in catering for homeless young people's HIV/AIDS health promotion needs? If so, what kinds of activities might it involve?

11.   What other kinds of support might homeless young
      people find acceptable and relevant to their HIV/
      AIDS health promotion needs?

CHAPTER ELEVEN

HIV/AIDS Education with Homeless Young People – Some Key Issues

Peter Aggleton and Ian Warwick

In the foreword to a recent report on homelessness published by the Faculty of Public Health Medicine of the Royal College of Physicians of the United Kingdom, Jocelyn Chamberlain concludes:

> . . . It is a cause for shame that a country as affluent as the UK should still be unable to guarantee housing for all its citizens. Moreover, the situation is getting worse, not better. Recent legislation has assisted those able to pay for their housing but has reduced the opportunity for decent housing for the poor, the unemployed and the mentally ill . . . Official statistics of homelessness only represent the tip of the iceberg of people who lack a secure dwelling place, and the size of the iceberg is increasing.
>
> (Faculty of Public Health Medicine, 1991)

As we have seen throughout this report, for young people the consequences of this state of affairs may be acute, especially for those who make their way to major cities in search of opportunity and employment. In this final chapter, we will reflect upon some of the themes which ran throughout the consultations organised by the Health Education Authority to identify key issues which need to be addressed, and solicit views on the priorities identified for future work.

Being 'homeless'

Problems arise in relation to understandings of what counts as homelessness. Commonsense encourages many people to think of homelessness as occurring when individuals:

a) find themselves quite literally without a roof over their heads;

b) are resident in temporary accommodation, insecurely or impermanently;

c) involuntarily share accommodation.

Legally, a person is homeless if she or he:

a) has no accommodation they are entitled to occupy;
b) has a home but is in danger of violence from someone living there;
c) is living in emergency or crisis accommodation;
d) is living in movable accommodation such as a caravan, but has nowhere to place it;
e) is part of a family separated because there is nowhere to live together.

In order to obtain permanent accommodation from a local authority, a person must be legally homeless, in priority need, and must not have become intentionally homeless. Priority need is defined in a number of ways, but includes situations where there are dependent children; when people have been made homeless through a disaster such as fire or flood; and when people are deemed vulnerable because of physical disability, mental ill-health, old age, domestic violence and other special reasons. Additionally, pregnant women are recognised as having priority need. Local authorities exercise considerable discretion in applying the law in relation to 'vulnerability' and there are major differences in practice across the country (Evans and Duncan, 1989; Niner, 1989).

The situation is particularly acute for homeless young people. It has recently been reported that only a fifth of British housing authorities were willing to regard them as vulnerable and therefore eligible for housing (National Children's Home, 1989). This point was supported by statements from a number of participants in the HEA's consultations, and came from representatives of both the statutory and voluntary sectors.

Understanding the nature of youth homelessness

In the popular imagination, youth homelessness is frequently understood to be the consequence of irresponsibility and an unwillingness to remain within the family home. Throughout the consultation, evidence was presented which shows that 'push' factors such as family violence, domestic discord, and physical, mental and sexual abuse are of increasing significance when it comes to explaining why many young people become homeless. This has consequences for the kind of support offered, since there may not only be issues of homelessness to consider, but also the aftermath of distressing and possibly abusive earlier experience.

Relatively large numbers of homeless young people have backgrounds in local authority care. For them, special support may be needed to provide opportunities for the development of the social skills necessary to secure housing and employment. It is of particular concern that such a large number of homeless young people involved in prostitution come from such backgrounds, and we need urgently to consider the most appropriate strategies to meet their HIV/AIDS health promotion needs. An empathetic, non-judgemental and confidential approach was advocated by consultation participants, which mediates between young people and existing services.

Working collaboratively

Throughout the consultations, there was much discussion of the challenges to intersectoral collaboration to meet the needs of homeless young people. Participants from voluntary agencies and non-governmental organisations made frequent reference to the difficulties they encountered liaising with statutory services. Young people themselves expressed such concerns, sometimes directly and sometimes through the voices of trusted workers. Hostility, prejudice and lack of understanding were common amongst those with whom they had come into contact. Non-judgemental and user-friendly services seemed much needed, operating at times and in contexts which homeless young people found accessible.

Particular difficulties seemed to arise in relation to the definitions of 'homelessness' employed by housing authorities, a point which echoes findings from a recent survey of housing authorities' interpretations of need (National Children's Home, 1989). Problems were seen as particularly acute in provincial and rural areas, and for those young people aged under 18. While the 1989 Children Act imposes a new duty on local authorities to provide accommodation for 16 to 17-year-olds if their welfare is prejudiced by homelessness, the loose wording of the Act makes interpretation uncertain. This was certainly the case in relation to earlier Codes of Guidance. The National Children's Home study referred to above found, for example, that only 40% of local authorities responding considered vulnerable 'a girl under 18 open to sexual and financial exploitation'; and this same survey found that almost three-quarters of housing authorities said they did not co-ordinate their work on homeless young people with social services departments. Clearly it will take time for this situation to change.

The role of education

While consultation participants differed from one another when identifying the nature of the health-related risks facing homeless young people, all agreed that an integrated approach was the best to adopt when undertaking health education with this group. If you are young and homeless, finding somewhere to stay, keeping warm, having enough money to eat, and getting a job take precedence over learning more about sexually transmitted diseases, injecting drug use and HIV and AIDS. Health promotion in the broadest sense is therefore needed, not health education *per se*.

While the foundations for this kind of work can be laid in schools, the present legal and political context makes it difficult to do so, at least in the eyes of many teachers. Consultation participants voiced concern about the effects of legislation such as Section 28 of the 1988 Local Government Act, which has been widely interpreted (incorrectly) as setting limits upon what teachers can and can not do in schools. Concern was also expressed about the extent to which school governing bodies in England and Wales were equipped to carry out their statutory responsibilities in relation to the formulation of policy on sex education, as well as about the extent to which teachers are adequately prepared for work in this field. How many of them, for example, are able to teach pragmatically rather than moralistically about the ways in which HIV-related risks can be reduced through safer sex and safer injecting drug use? Interventions were seen as being urgently needed to provide teachers with the necessary skills and dispositions to carry out this work effectively and non-judgementally.

Work out of school is also essential, and some important initiatives are now under way using outreach and detached work to meet homeless young people's needs. Peer-led education is being used as well, although this requires structure, training, supervision and support. It is not as simple as saying to young people, get on and do it. That way, all manner of confusion can arise, and prejudicial and discriminatory attitudes may well be reinforced. Nevertheless, such out-of-school work may more genuinely meet the needs of those who are young and homeless. Some young people's disenchantment with formal educational provision makes them suspicious of any intervention which harks back to school. Examination of those strategies which prove most effective in meeting young people's needs is urgently required.

The policy context

Interventions such as those identified above are unlikely to succeed unless steps are taken to simplify and rationalise public policy in relation to housing. While the underlying cause of homelessness, amongst young and old alike, is the mismatch between the need for and supply of affordable decent housing (Faculty of Public Health Medicine, 1991), the situation for young people is exacerbated by the fact that their housing rights are governed by legislative provision as diverse as the 1986 Social Security Act, the 1988 Housing Act and the 1989 Children Act. Framed for different purposes, and in response to differing political and administrative priorities, these Acts establish a complex terrain within which local authority and social service workers operate. It is little wonder, therefore, that workers in specialist agencies, as well as young people themselves, are often confused about their rights and uncertain how to access services.

A way forward?

Throughout the discussion and consultation described in this report a number of issues arose which it is essential to address if progress is to be made in this important area of work. These include questions concerning the relative responsibilities of different authorities, organisations, associations and agencies in initiating and progressing HIV/AIDS education with homeless young people. Intersectoral and inter-agency collaboration will be essential if future work is to succeed. The following questions may be helpful in focusing future discussion and debate. They are of particular relevance to policy makers, managers and workers in each of the fields identified and offer the basis for an agenda for effective action.

Health authorities

- How might assessment of homeless young people's HIV/AIDS health education needs best be conducted?
- How might access to health services be improved for homeless young people?
- What are the most effective styles of outreach work with homeless young people?
- How might other service providers (for example, voluntary organisations/other statutory bodies) best be supported in the work they do?
- What are the most effective forms of liaison and co-ordination between health authorities and other bodies?

Local authorities

Housing departments

- What are the best ways of finding out about the HIV/AIDS health education needs of homeless young people?
- What are the best ways of identifying the HIV/AIDS education training needs of local authority housing workers?
- What are the most appropriate ways of training staff who work with homeless young people?
- How might housing legislation best be interpreted so as to meet the HIV/AIDS health needs of homeless young people?
- What are the most effective ways of undertaking collaborative work within and across local authority boundaries?

Social services

- How might the HIV/AIDS education needs of homeless young people, or young people being looked after by local authorities, best be identified?
- What are the most appropriate kinds of training for adults who work with homeless young people, or those at greater risk of becoming homeless? Such adults include residential care workers, foster carers, social workers.
- What are the most effective forms of HIV/AIDS education in residential care and supported housing schemes?
- Is HIV/AIDS peer-led education appropriate in residential settings or supported lodgings?
- How might legislation (for example, the Children Act) best be interpreted to meet the HIV/AIDS health needs of homeless young people, or those at greater risk of becoming homeless?
- What are the most effective ways of undertaking collaborative work within and across local authority boundaries and with other bodies?

Housing associations

- How might the HIV/AIDS education needs of young people in housing association accommodation best be identified?
- What are the most appropriate ways of identifying the HIV/AIDS training needs of housing association staff (for example, managers of shared housing, Special Needs Officers)?
- Is HIV/AIDS peer-led education appropriate for young people living in shared accommodation?
- What are the most effective ways of facilitating collaborative working with other bodies?

Voluntary organisations

Providers of accommodation for homeless young people

- What are the most appropriate ways of facilitating collaborative working with other bodies?
- What are the most effective ways of training workers?
- Is HIV/AIDS peer-led education appropriate for young people living in hostels or other shared-living settings?
- What are the most useful forms of support that statutory

bodies can give to voluntary organisations providing accommodation?
- What are the most effective forms of collaborative work?

Providers of HIV/AIDS education

- In what ways can the HIV/AIDS education needs of homeless young people best be identified?
- How can voluntary sector providers of HIV/AIDS education to homeless young people be best supported in their work by statutory bodies?
- What are the most effective ways of collaborative working?
- How might the experience of these service providers best inform purchasing priorities?

Other voluntary groups with expertise in housing/homelessness issues and/or HIV/AIDS education

- How might these groups best be supported in identifying the HIV/AIDS health promotion needs of homeless young people?
- In what ways can the expertise of these groups best inform the development of policy for HIV/AIDS education with homeless young people?

References

Faculty of Public Health Medicine (1991) *Housing or Homelessness: A Public Health Perspective*. London, Faculty of Public Health Medicine, Royal Colleges of Physicians of the UK.

Evans, A. and Duncan, S. (1989) *Responding to Homelessness: Local Authority Policy and Practice*. London, HMSO.

Niner, P. (1989) *Homelessness in Nine Local Authorities: Case Studies of Policy and Practice*. London, HMSO.

National Children's Home (1989) *Housing Vulnerable Young Single Homeless People*. London, National Children's Home.

Consultation Participants

Peter Aggleton, Health and Education Research Unit, Goldsmiths' College, University of London; Mike Ashley, Association of District Councils; Alan Baldwin, Youthlink, Birmingham; Una Barry, Centrepoint Soho; Claire Barron, All-Party Parliamentary Group on AIDS; Hilary Bird, Department of Housing and Property Services, Lambeth; Derek Bodell, Health Education Authority; Ray Boyce, Social Services Department, Westminster City Council; Ailsa Butler, All-Party Parliamentary Group on AIDS; Dennis Carney, Black HIV/AIDS Network; Liza Catan, Research Development Division, Department of Health; Jimi Christmas, Central London Action on Street Health; Hannah Cinamon, HIV/AIDS and Sexual Health Programme, Health Education Authority; George Clarke, Research Division, Department of the Environment; Nicholas Clarke, Youthmatters; Suzie Daniel, Teenage Health Centre Development Project, Nottingham; Lynn Cowan, Greater Glasgow Health Board; Alan Davey, Department of Social Security; Police Sgt Keith Donovan, Digbeth Police Station; Hugh Dufficy, Standing Conference on Drug Abuse; Ailsa Duncan, West Berkshire Health Authority; Roger Gaitley, British Association of Social Workers; Casey Galloway, Frontliners; Colin Glover, The London Connection; Barbara Gibson, Streetwise Youth, London; Heidi Gilhooly, Childline; Judith Green, National Youth Agency; Naomi Honigsbaum, National Children's Bureau; Joan Holmes, Yorkshire Health Authority; Lauren Jackson, Terrence Higgins Trust; Jim Jeall, Social Science Inspectorate; Andrea Kelmanson, National AIDS Trust; Hilary Kinnell, Central Birmingham Health Authority; Mark Kjeldsen, Streetwise Youth; Charles McIlwrich, Police Federation of England and Wales; Paul McKeown, Centrepoint, London; Cheryl Marsh, The Polish Centre; Gary Mead, Shelter; Michelle Monks, NAYPIC; Danny Morris, Soho Project; Reena Mukherji, Piccadilly Advice Centre; Paul O'Brien, The Police Federation of England and Wales; Brendan O'Mahoney, Barnardo's, London; Roz Pendlebury, AIDS and Housing Project, London; Nancy Perrin, New

Horizon Youth Centre; Fiona Phillipson, Bridges Project, Edinburgh; Lisa Power, Association of London Authorities; Gary Quarless, Nottingham Health Authority; Martin Raymond, Scottish Health Education Group; David Rivett, Health Education Authority; Lesley Reid, Lothian Health Board; Hugh Robertson, NALGO; Jackie Robinson, Commission for Racial Equality; Pepe Roche, Youthlink, Birmingham; Robin Sequeira, Association of County Councils; Julia Shelley, Landmark; Jaswant Singh; Michael Narayn Singh, Manchester City Council; Major Trevor Smith, The Salvation Army; Bob Stead, Research and Development Section, Lothian Region Social Work Department; Noeline Thomas, Health Promotion Authority for Wales; John Thompson, AIDS Unit, Department of Health; David Tomlinson, Department of Genito-Urinary Medicine, St Mary's Hospital; Brian Travers, Soho Project; Duncan Tree, Association of County Councils; Clive Turner, Central Council for Education and Training in Social Work; Ian Warwick, Health and Education Research Unit, Goldsmiths' College, University of London; Br Colin Wilfred, London Churches HIV/AIDS Unit; Mark Wilkinson, West Berkshire Health Authority; Ruth Williams, Resource.

Consultation chairs

Joan Lestor MP; Lisa Power, Association of London Authorities; Simon White, Hammersmith and Fulham Social Services Department.